Crocodarling

Story and pictures by
MARY RAYNER

BRADBURY PRESS
New York

For Matthew, Jack and Joshua

Bradbury Press
An Affiliate of Macmillan, Inc.
866 Third Avenue, New York, N.Y. 10022
Made and Printed in Great Britain

10 9 8 7 6 5 4 3 2 1

Library of Congress Cataloging in Publication Data
Rayner, Mary.
    Crocodarling.
    Summary: Sam's friend Crocodarling goes with
him everywhere and helps him out of some difficult
situations, especially in school.
    [1. Toys — Fiction.   2. Schools — Fiction]
I. Title.
PZ7.R2315Cr 1986 [E] 85-11395
ISBN 0-02-775770-6

Sam woke up one morning with the sun shining
into his room. Crocodarling was still asleep on
his pillow.

"Wake up," Sam said, very soft. "It's school
again today."

Crocodarling opened his mouth in a big
toothy smile. "So it is. Better get up."

They got up and Sam began to dress. Mom came upstairs to help, bringing Graham with her. They went down for breakfast.

Mom set a place for Sam, a place for Graham, a place for herself and a place for Crocodarling.

"Would you like some oatmeal?" she asked.

"Crocodarling doesn't like oatmeal," said Sam.

"All right," said Mom. "No oatmeal. Only for Graham and me. Do you want an egg?"

"Crocodarling wants one too," said Sam.

"Right," said Mom. "Three eggs. One for you, one for Graham, one for Crocodarling," and she put them in a pan of boiling water and turned on the timer.

"Drink your milk, Sam."

"I don't like milk," said Sam.
"Just a little," said Mom.
Sam drank a little.

After breakfast they walked to Sam's school.

"Hurry up," said Mom.

"Crocodarling can't hurry up," said Sam.
"The pavement hurts his feet."

Mom waited.

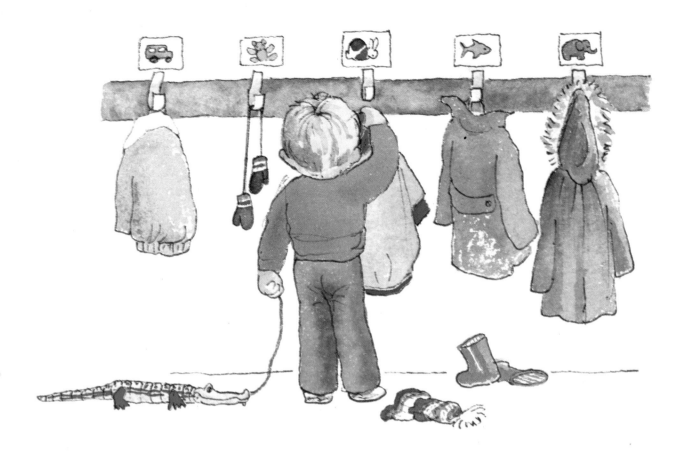

In school Sam hung up his coat, and Mom kissed him good bye.

"Kiss Crocodarling," he said.

Mom blew Crocodarling a kiss. Then she left.

Susan and Sally were painting on the easel.

"Hello, Sam," said the teacher.

"I want to paint," said Sam.

"Come and play with the blocks,
and then you can paint," said the teacher.

"Now," said Sam.

"What was that?"

"Crocodarling said *now*."

"Well, tell him he must wait
his turn," said the teacher.

Sam stood behind Sally. Sally's jar of yellow paint
fell over.

"My painting is ruined!" she shouted.

"Who did that?" asked the teacher. "Was that you, Sam?"

"No," said Sam, very loud.

"Oh yes it was," said Henry. "I saw him.
He pushed it over."

"Sam, I think you had better go play out in the sandbox," said the teacher.

Sally and Susan smiled. The teacher gave Sally a new jar of yellow paint and a clean sheet of paper. Sam went out into the sandbox, taking Crocodarling with him.

He made a tall castle. Crocodarling thought it was terrific.

Henry came to play in the sandbox, and put his foot on Sam's castle. Sam did nothing. Henry kicked the tower down.

Crocodarling opened his jaws, and lashed his tail at Henry.

"Get out!" shouted Sam, very loud.
"That was my castle."

To Sam's surprise Henry got out. Sam had just
finished making another tower when it was time
for milk and crackers.

Sam ate two crackers and took
two more for Crocodarling.

"You're not drinking your
milk, Sam," said the teacher.
"What's the matter?"

Sam said nothing. Crocodarling
said nothing. Crocodarling knew.
The cup fell over.
    "Who did that?" asked the teacher.
    "Not me," said Sam.
    "Are you sure, Sam? Are you
telling the truth?"
    "Well, it might have been
Crocodarling, with his tail."

The teacher said nothing. Sally, Susan, Sarita and Maurice were staring at Sam.

Then the teacher said, "If Crocodarling isn't more careful with his tail, he won't be able to come to school with you. Do you understand, Sam?"

Sally, Susan and Sarita smiled wide smiles. Sam walked over to the Lego box to play.

"Cheer up, Sam," said Crocodarling, very soft. "We'll make a Lego car." So they did.

Then the teacher clapped her hands. Sam turned around. "Come on, Sam. It's your turn to paint."

Sam looked for his Lego car to take to
the easel, but Henry was pushing it along the
floor, *brrm, brrm.*

"Come along, Sam, you wanted to paint.
Now you're dilly-dallying."

Sam picked up Crocodarling and went
to the easel.

"I don't know what to paint,"
Sam said.

"Paint the school," said the teacher, "and all your friends."

"Can I put in Crocodarling?" asked Sam.
The teacher sighed. "Oh, all right."

Sam drew.

The teacher looked at Sam's painting. "That's nice. Why don't you draw your friends. They would fit down there."

Sam did. Crocodarling thought it was terrific.

Mom came to get Sam. She helped him put on his
coat. The teacher rolled up Sam's
picture and gave it to Mom. Mom put it on
top of Graham's stroller.

On the way home Mom said, "What did you do at school?"

"Played in the sandbox," said Sam.

"Oh," said Mom. "Who did you play with?"

"Crocodarling."

"Wasn't there anyone else?" asked Mom.

"Henry was there."

"How nice. Is Henry your friend? Perhaps we can ask him home to play."

"Crocodarling doesn't like Henry," said Sam, and he picked up Crocodarling and ran on ahead.

"Wait!" shouted Mom, very loud. "Watch the road!"

"I can't wait. Crocodarling wants to hurry. I have to catch up with him."

Mom hurried, too, to catch up with Sam.

That evening, after Graham had had his bath
and been put to bed, Mom read Sam a story.
Crocodarling listened, too. When Mom kissed
Sam good night, Sam said, "Kiss Crocodarling
too."

"Good night Crocodarling," said Mom.
She turned out the light but left the door
open. Sam heard her going downstairs. It was
dark. "Mom!" he called out.

"It's all right," said Crocodarling, very soft. "I won't go to sleep till you have."

Mom came back into the room. "Come on, Sam, I've had enough of this today. *Now* what's the matter?" She turned the light back on.

Sam said nothing. Crocodarling said nothing. Crocodarling knew. Then Sam said, "You forgot to look at my picture."

"So I did." Mom unrolled the picture and pinned it up on the wall. "There!"

She looked at it. "What is it?"

"It's my school."

"Oh, I see," said Mom. "That must be the teacher. Is this Sally? And Susan?"

"Yes."

"And is this Sarita with the pigtails?"

"Yes," said Sam. "Crocodarling's going to play with her tomorrow. And that's Simon and that's Martin and that's Maurice."

"Who's that?" asked Mom.

"That's me."

She counted. "One, two, three, four, five, six, seven — only seven children. What's this?"

"Crocodarling, of course," said Sam.

"Oh," said Mom, peering at the picture. "He looks very fat. Where's Henry?"

Sam said nothing. Crocodarling said nothing.
Crocodarling knew.

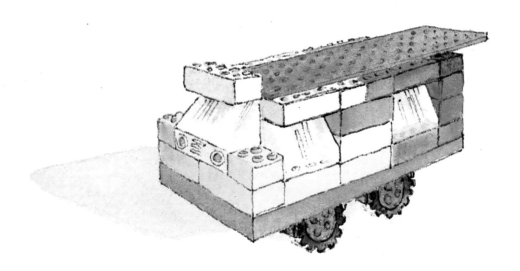

The next morning Crocodarling went to school with Sam again. Sam and Sarita played with the Lego, and Crocodarling watched. Sam made another car, and he and Sarita made a garage for it, and then they drove it in and out, *brrm, brrm*. Crocodarling thought it was terrific.

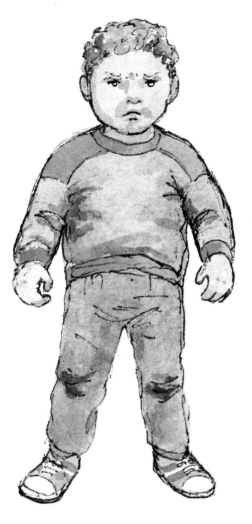

Henry said, "That's my car. I was playing with it yesterday."

Sam held onto the car, tight, and said, "No, it's mine. I made it."

Henry hit Sam.

Sam hit Henry.
Henry fell over.

Henry cried, very loud.

The teacher said, "Sam, are you fighting?"
Sam said nothing. Sally and Susan
and Maurice and Martin and Simon and
Sarita and Crocodarling were ALL
staring at Henry.

The teacher helped Henry up and wiped his eyes.
"All right, who started it?"

"Henry!" they all shouted.

The teacher said, "Well, then, Henry will help me
clean up, and the rest of you may go and play
outside. Who made this car? It's terrific."

Sam picked up Crocodarling, smiling a wide smile.
"Me," he said.